With Love,
Hope

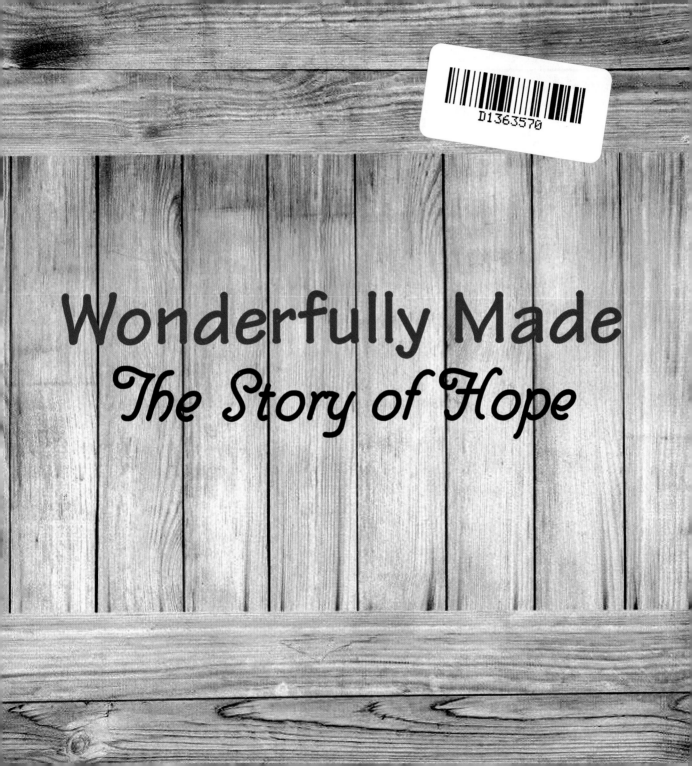

Wonderfully Made
The Story of Hope

Author Laurie Bell is a retired elementary teacher and founder of the non-profit outreach, Mini Joys. Sweet, gentle, minis and big-hearted volunteers partner together to teach impactful life lessons and to spread joy, hope, and healing to those facing tough challenges.

The Mini Joys crew wants you to enjoy this story and to always remember that YOU are wonderfully made!

Dedication

Do you ever wish you were stronger, smarter, taller, or prettier? How about thinner, athletic, popular, or more confident?

Do you ever hope for smaller ears, a better nose, bigger muscles, or a more beautiful voice? The wish list goes on and on.

Maybe you dream of greatness but often feel unimportant or invisible.

If you find yourself wishing you could change who you are, or at times you just long to be more like "everyone else," then this book is dedicated to you. I guess this little book is for just about all of us!

My name is Hope, and I am a miniature donkey. Although I am only a youngster, I have already learned something wonderful that has made each day so much sweeter. I would like to tell you my story. . .

When I was just a baby, weaned and ready to leave my mom, I went to live with a nice family. They took me to my new home which was a tiny little ranch in the foothills just outside of town.

It was a lovely, peaceful place, but it didn't take me long to realize that I was different than the rest of the herd.

My new owners were kind to me and took very good care of all of us. I joined Levi, Sophie, and Spunky who were all miniature horses. They weren't too sure exactly what I was, and they spent many of the first days and weeks staring at me from a distance. I felt lonely.

Although each of the minis were a different color, to me they all looked and sounded alike. I stood out!

I was given the name "Hope" and soon thought that I knew the reason for my name. I began to spend most of my time hoping that I could be less like me and more like my new family of miniature horses. I didn't like anything about myself.

"If only I could be just like everyone else," I daydreamed. I did not like standing out in the herd!

Why couldn't I have a long, thick, beautiful mane like Spunky? My mohawk-style mane looks the same every day. There's nothing to brush, braid, or shine. A beautiful mane might make me feel special.

If I couldn't have his mane, how about his striking blue eyes? Mine are gray and dull, blending in with my boring, shaggy, gray coat.

I wished that I could have an awesome tail like Sophie's. It's white and sparkles in the sun. It almost reaches the ground and blows in the wind when she runs.

My spindly little tail bone is barely covered with hair. I was glad that I didn't have to see it much!

I was so jealous of Levi's cute, little ears! One of my biggest hopes was that one morning I would wake up and my big, silly-looking ears would be gone. I wasn't sure where they would go, but just so they were not on the top of my head anymore.

I spent hours and hours looking at Levi's tiny, little ears and just wishing we could trade. How did he get so lucky?

16

I would have given anything to get rid of my obnoxious "hee-haw!" You could hear it all the way down the road. It seemed that everyone stopped and stared—my human friends, the family dogs, all of the horses, and every squirrel, owl, and hawk on the ranch.

If only I had a beautiful little whinny that everyone loved to hear. I thought that would have made me happy!

Eventually, we became too busy for me to spend as many hours daydreaming. The minis and I did a lot of visiting with human friends. Some came to our barn to see us, but often we were off to visit them.

We went to schools, hospitals, parks, boys and girls clubs, senior centers, and shelter homes. What adventures we had! I have learned something very important.

On our visits, I noticed that
every new human friend we met was
different than the one we met before.

Some were tall. Some were short.
There were thin kids and rounder kids.
There were loud kids and quiet kids.
Children who ran, skipped, and jumped,
and others who sat very still and
loved on us ever so gently.

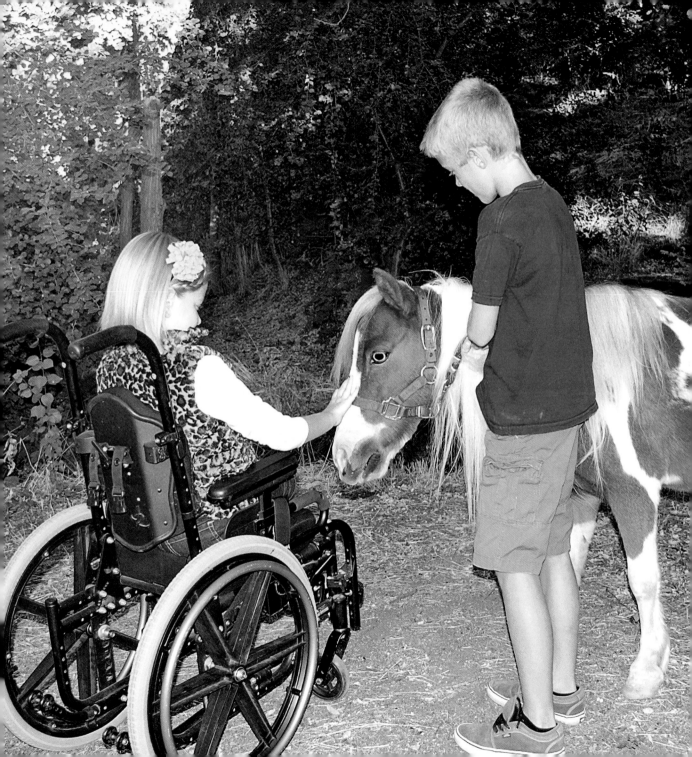

In fact, not one of my new human friends was alike: whether old, young, lots of hair, no hair, big, small, strong, or fragile. Each one had their own look, shape, sound, and movements.

I could visit people all day long and still not find two who were the same. I never got tired of meeting new friends because getting to know each one brought fun surprises.

Meeting all those people changed my thoughts. Now, I realize that life would be rather boring if everyone I met was alike.

I don't think that our human friends would have as much fun either if Levi, Sophie, Spunky, and I were all the same. Spending time with each one of us seems to bring them joy. I think it is because we each have something special that makes us just who we are.

I guess these big ears of mine are just a part of what makes me, ME! My little spindly tail, mohawk-style mane, and shaggy, gray coat all help to make me, ME!

And let's not forget my very loud "hee-haw!" There's not another ME on our whole ranch. In fact, there's not another ME anywhere! That's pretty awesome, don't you think?

I am so excited about what I've learned! I am not going to waste another minute hoping to be just like everyone else! That's not at all why I was named "Hope."

I finally know why they gave me this special name. It is certainly good to have hope, but from now on I am going to spend my time hoping in a whole new way…

Now, my hope is to be all that I was meant to be! No more hoping to be someone else. I was not an accident. I am here for a reason, and I want to be the best ME that I can be. Now that is worth hoping for!

I have learned that I am wonderfully made and I hope you know that you are, too! Please don't waste another minute. It's time to celebrate being the best YOU that you can be!

I promise this will make your days much brighter and you'll have more joy to share along the way!

Mini Joys, Inc.

Mini Joys is a charitable organization (501C-3) whose purpose is to promote joy, hope, and healing through programs using compassionate, gentle, miniature horses and big-hearted volunteers for those facing physical, mental, or emotional challenges.

It all began in 2009 in Boise, Idaho. A growing number of diverse groups have been served in southwest Idaho since that time with a primary focus on at-risk youth, and children in special education settings.

Teaching programs are designed for each target group and include lesson topics such as Caring for Animals, Friendship, Building Trust, Anti-Bullying, Growing in Confidence, and learning that each individual is unique and wonderfully made!

The Mini Joys horses and volunteers are frequent guests in area shelter homes and special education school classrooms. Various programs are also held at the Mini Ranch in the foothills just outside of Boise.

The horses can work alongside a counselor, teacher, social worker, physical, occupational, or speech therapist further broadening the goals and outcomes of the child-horse interaction.

Sometimes, the minis awesome "job" is simply to spread joy at senior residence homes, children's hospitals, veterans homes, and at other local nonprofit organization's special events.

Thank you for your support of the Mini Joys outreach programs!

minijoys.org

email: minijoys@live.com or visit: Mini Joys on Facebook